C000154255

Creative Scribbles

Parragon

Bath • New York • Singapore • Hong Kong • Cologne • Delhi
Melbourne • Amsterdam • Johannesburg • Auckland • Shenzhen

'There is
in seeing what
texture and tone
produce merely
and a bottle of

something magical you can do; what and colour you can with a pen point ink.’ **Ida Rentoul Outhwaite.**

a
y

Fill this page with **circles.**

Can you see a pattern within your image?

Fill this page with **SQUARES.**
How is your pattern different?

Fill these pages with your

doodles.

Space for your

creativity.

Rank the **SEVEN COLOURS** of the rainbow.

What does your personal rainbow look like? Draw it.

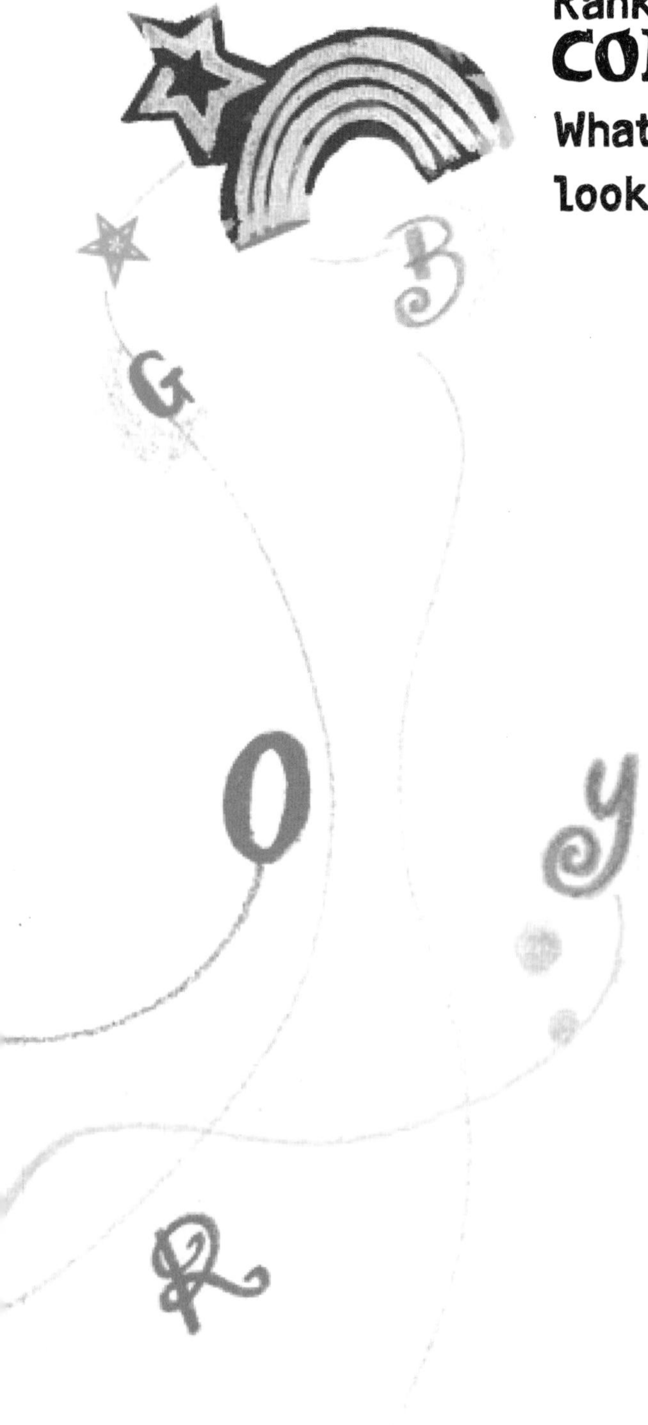

Red,
Orange,
Yellow,
Green,
Blue,
Indigo,
Violet.

I

Shade these pages and then use a rubber to cut lines through it.

Create your own **paisley** pattern.

'Colour is my obsession, joy

day-long and torment.'

Claude Monet.

Draw without

RESTRICTIONS.

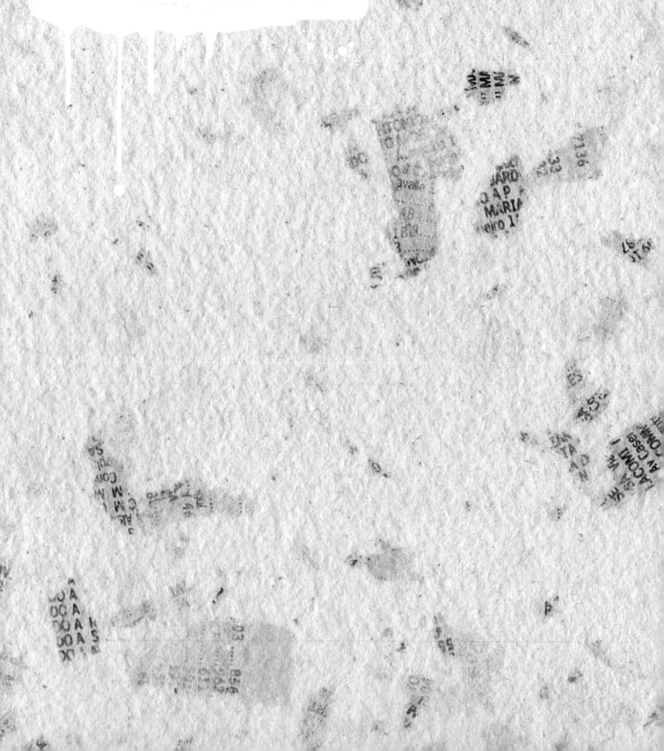

Play with spiralling lines.

Slice the page with DIAGONAL lines.

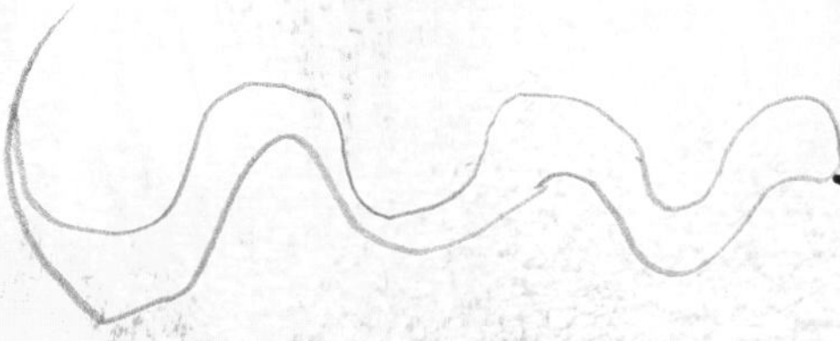

Try drawing just wavy lines.

Experiment with ZIGZAGGED lines.

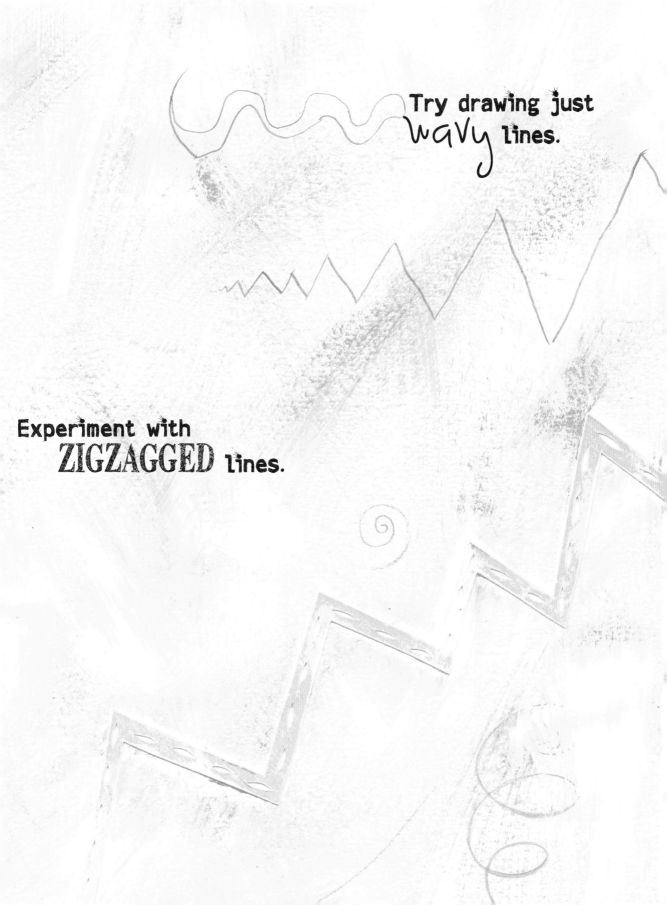

SKETCH!

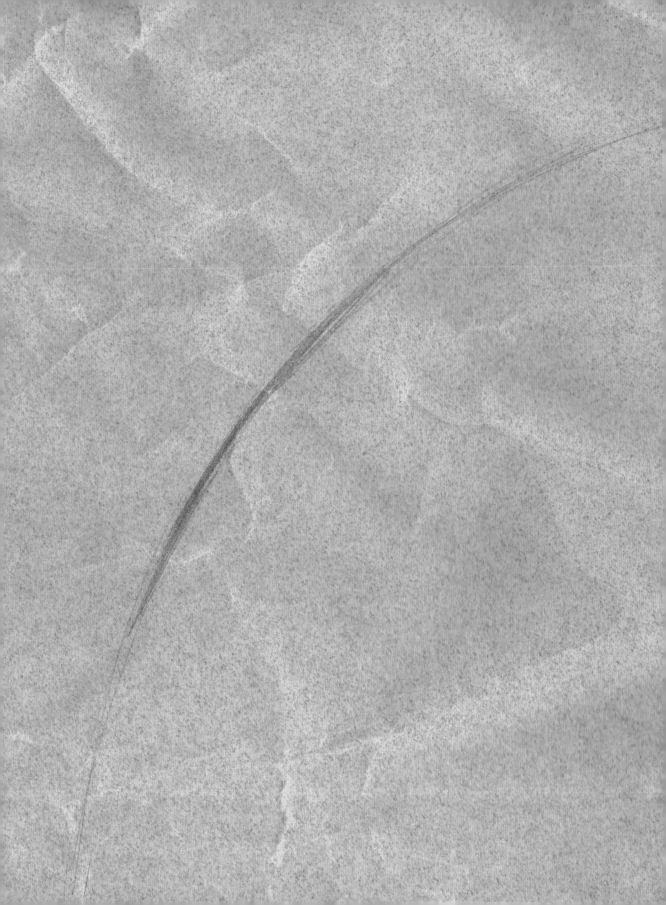

Pick a **colour.**

Look around and draw what you see of that colour.

Create a pattern using symbols from your

COMPUTER KEYBOARD.

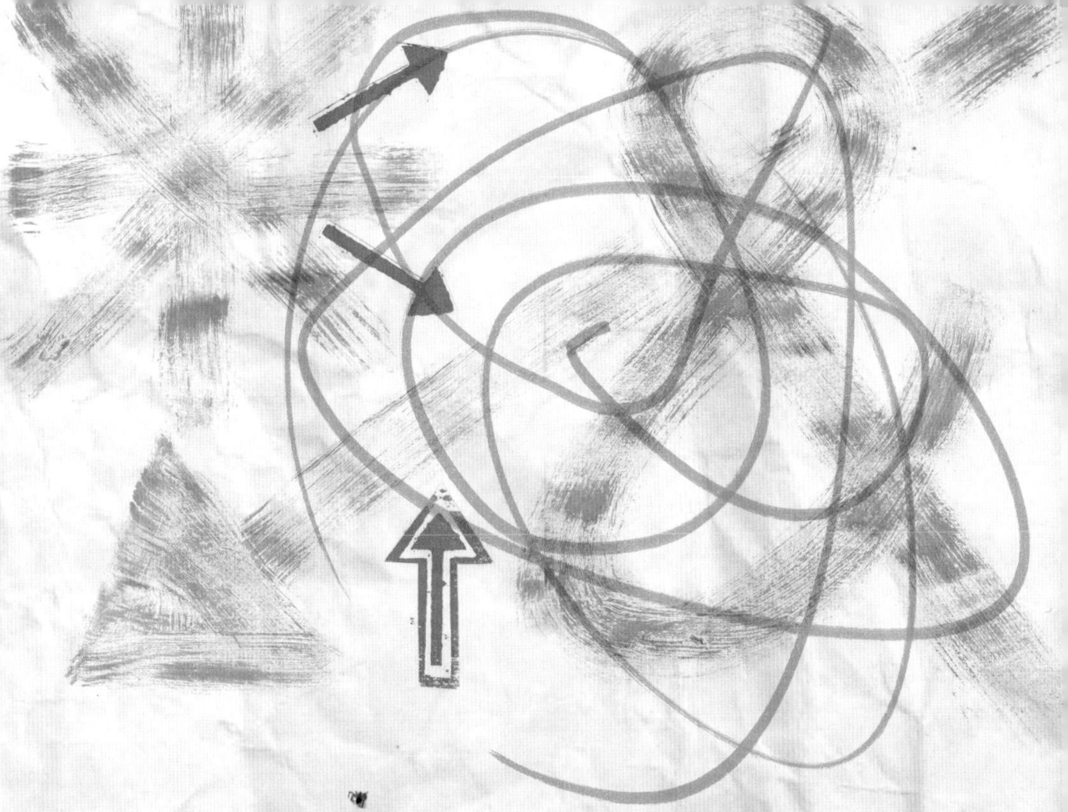

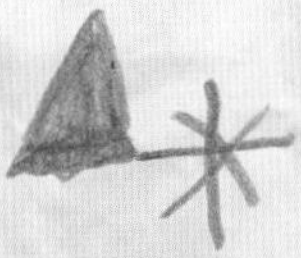

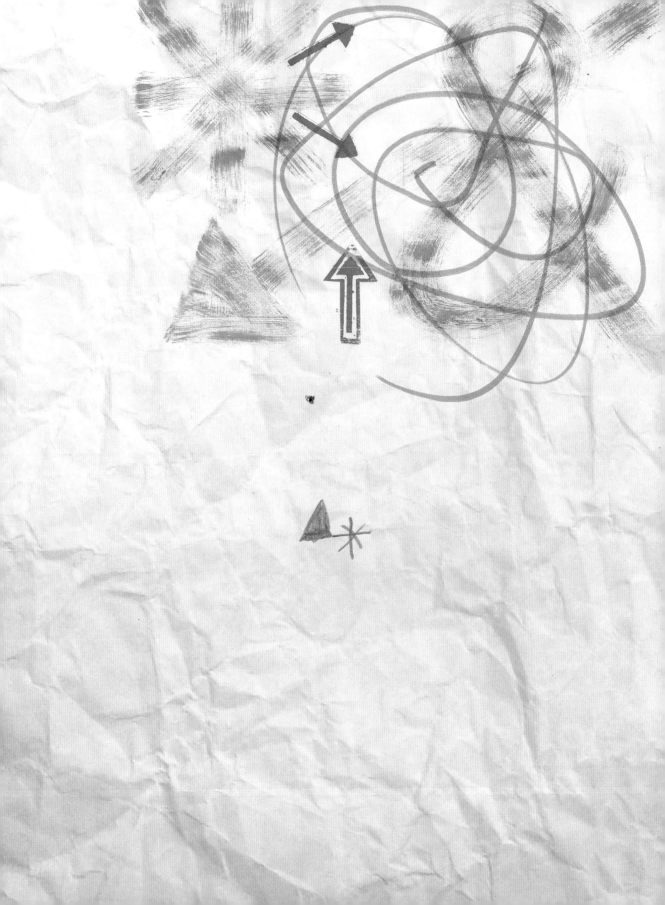

COLOUR these pages.

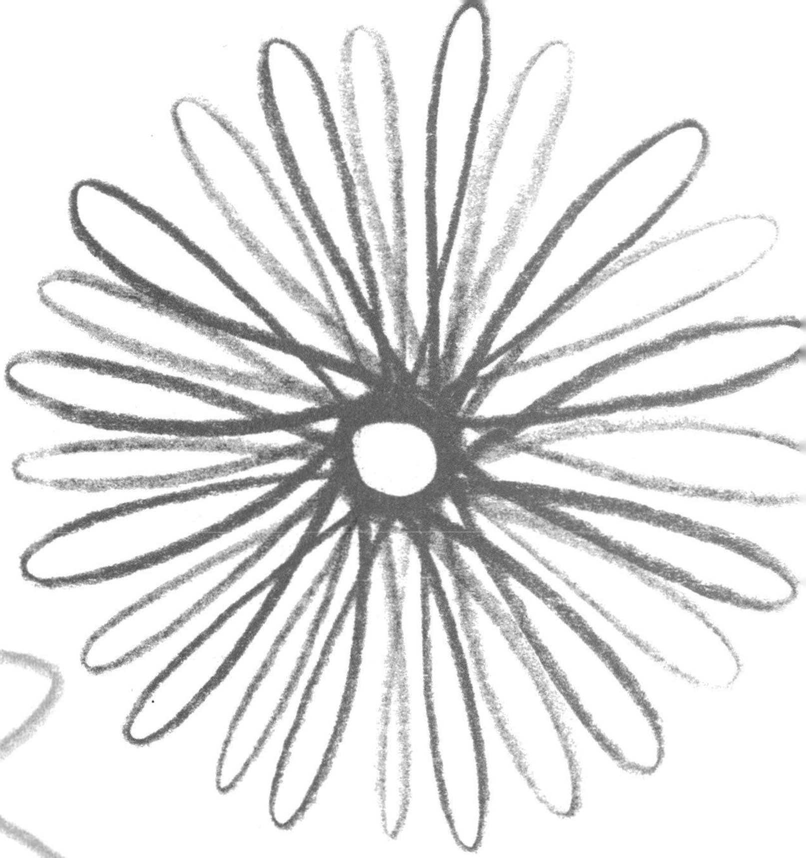

Doodle!

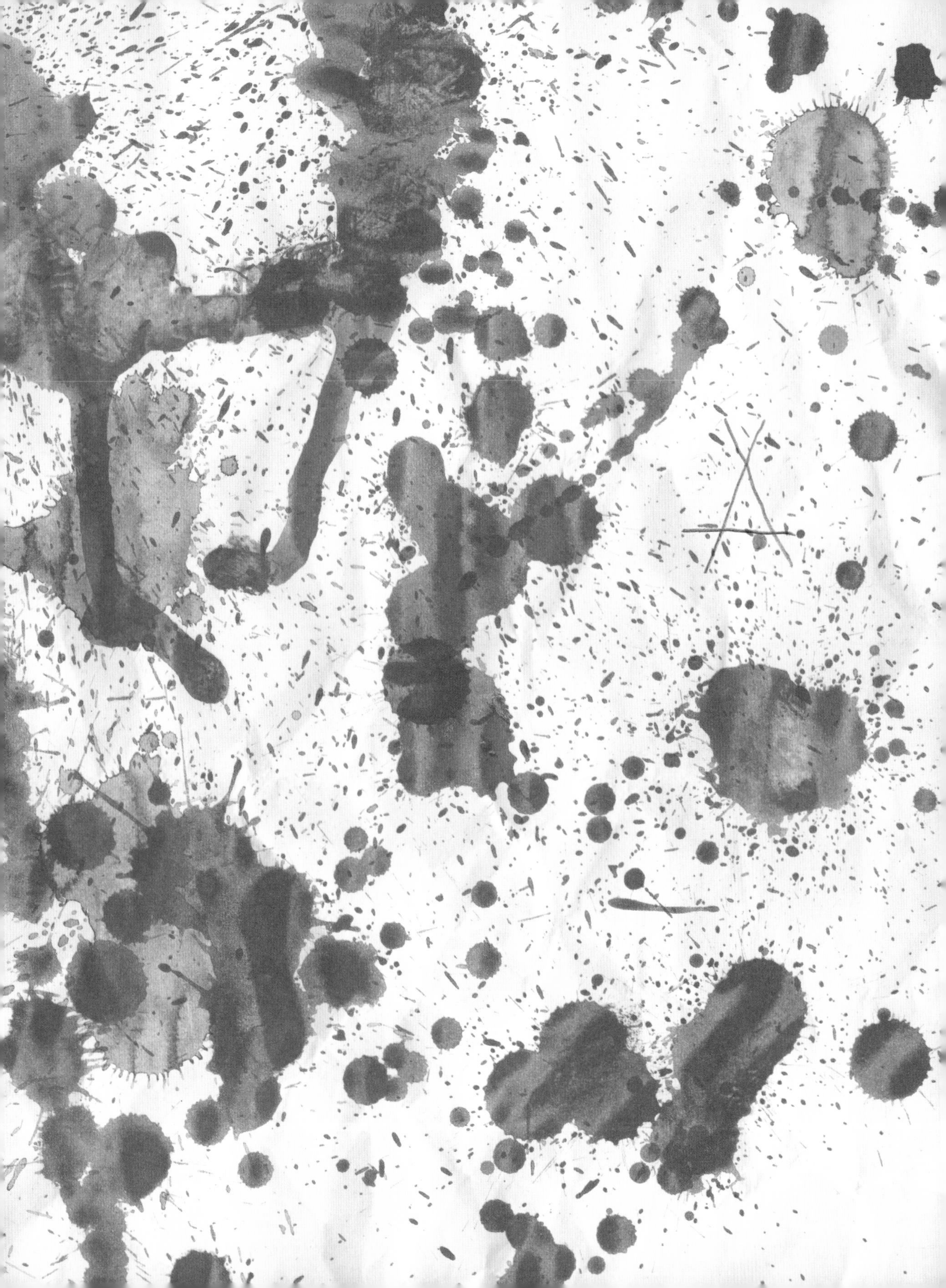

Fill these pages with music...

Using this graph paper create a **MOSAIC** using as many colours as you can.

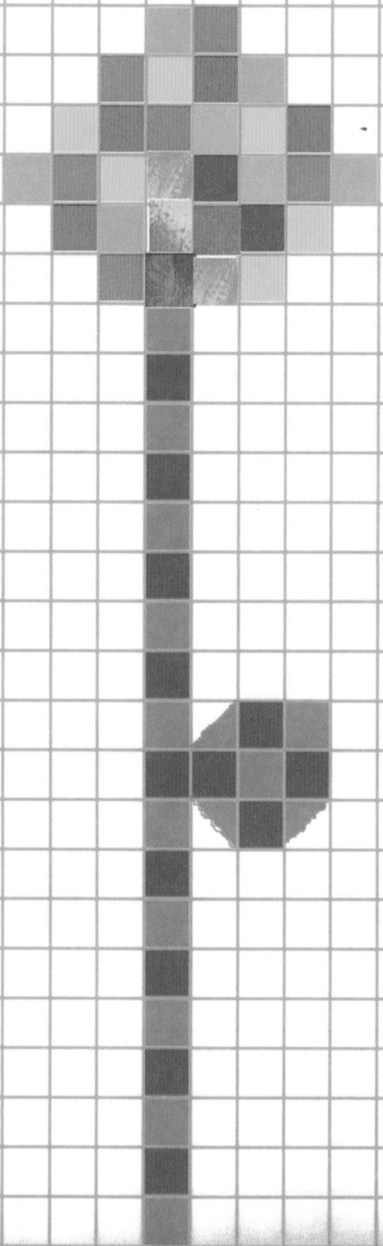

Create a list of words

about wood.

Carve those words into a
wood grain image.

Eleanor
Eleanor.
Eleanor
EleanoR
eleanor
eleanor
Eleanor
ELEANOR

Moss
moss
Moss

Write your **name** over and over, in different **STYLES** and **SIZES**, does it become anything different?

Don’t think, just draw.

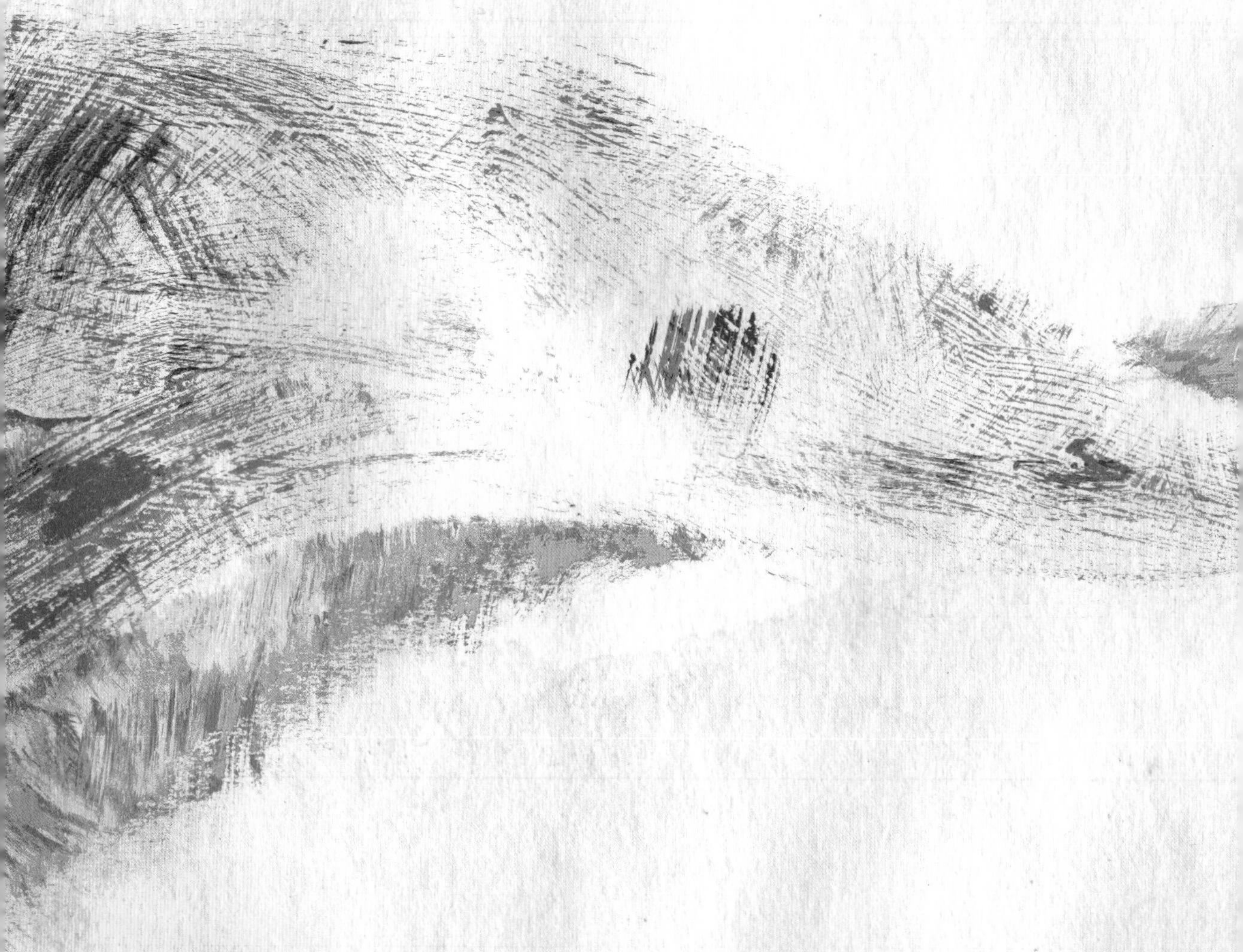

Draw something secret, then **cut it out** and hide it.

Using a single line draw a SKYLINE.

'I PAINT OBJECTS AS I THINK THEM, NOT AS I SEE THEM.'

Pablo Picasso.

Draw different shapes from your

imagination.

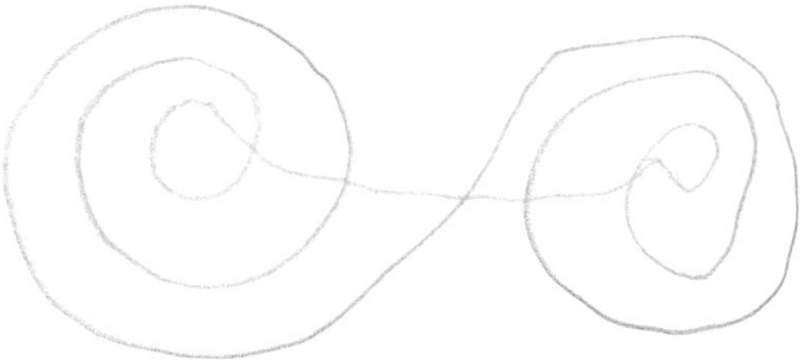

Draw something that begins with the letter

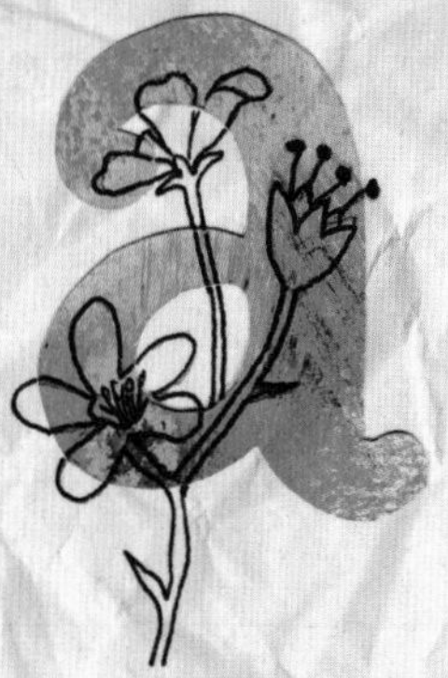

Draw something
that begins
with the letter Z

Sketch anything.

Your space.

Fill these pages with

birds in flight.

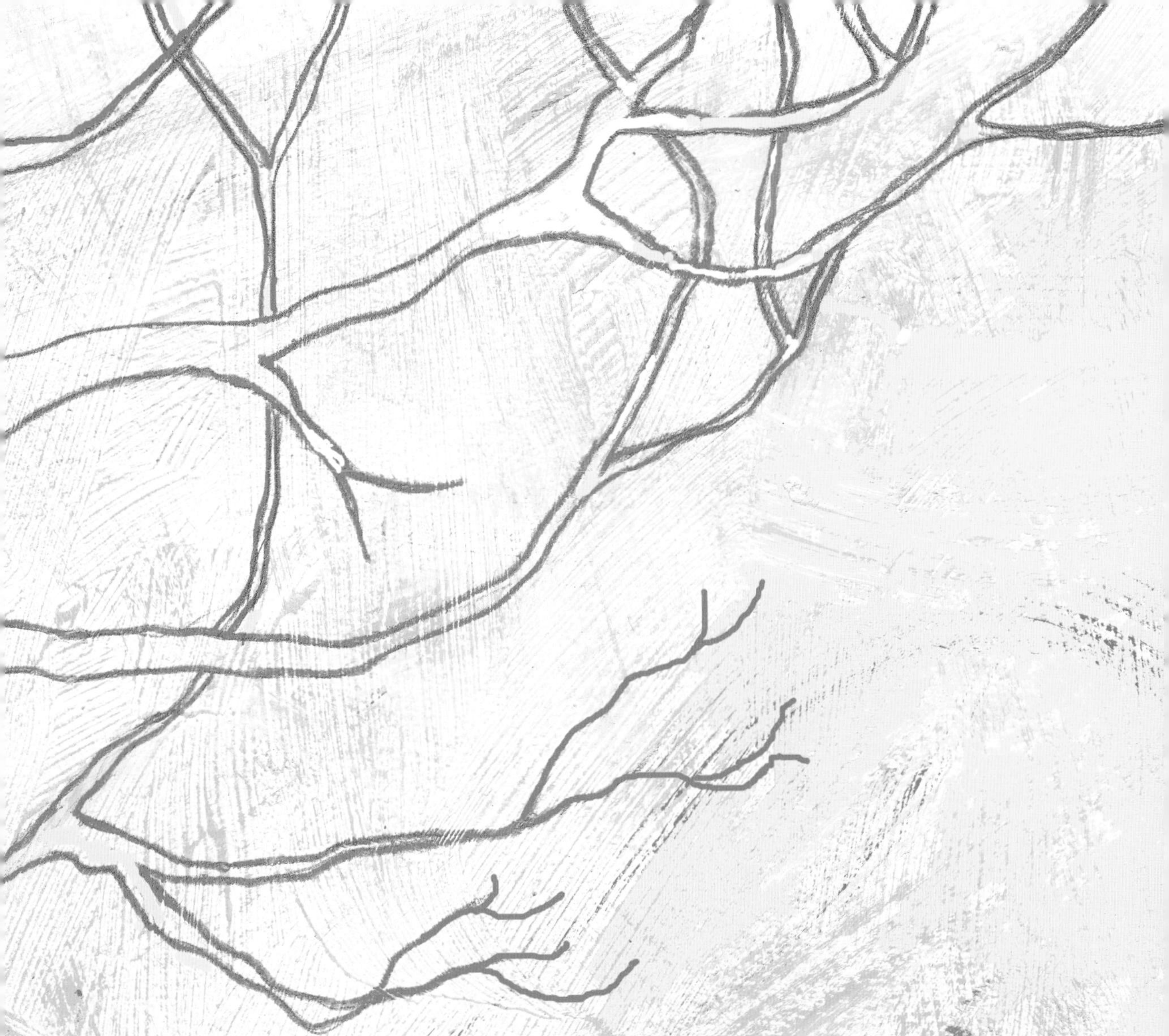

Fill this TREE with leaves and life.

Draw a picture of your favourite things in only your **favourite colour.**

Draw some

monsters.

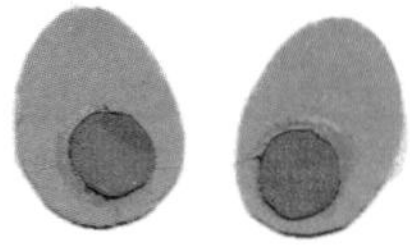

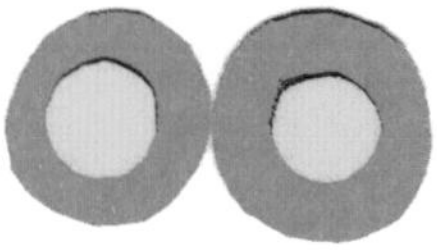

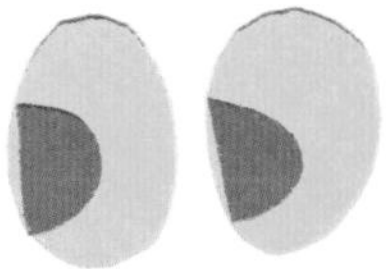

There are no limits.

Draw something **TALL.**

Draw something small.

In PRIMARY COLOURS only, draw the view from your window.

Draw!

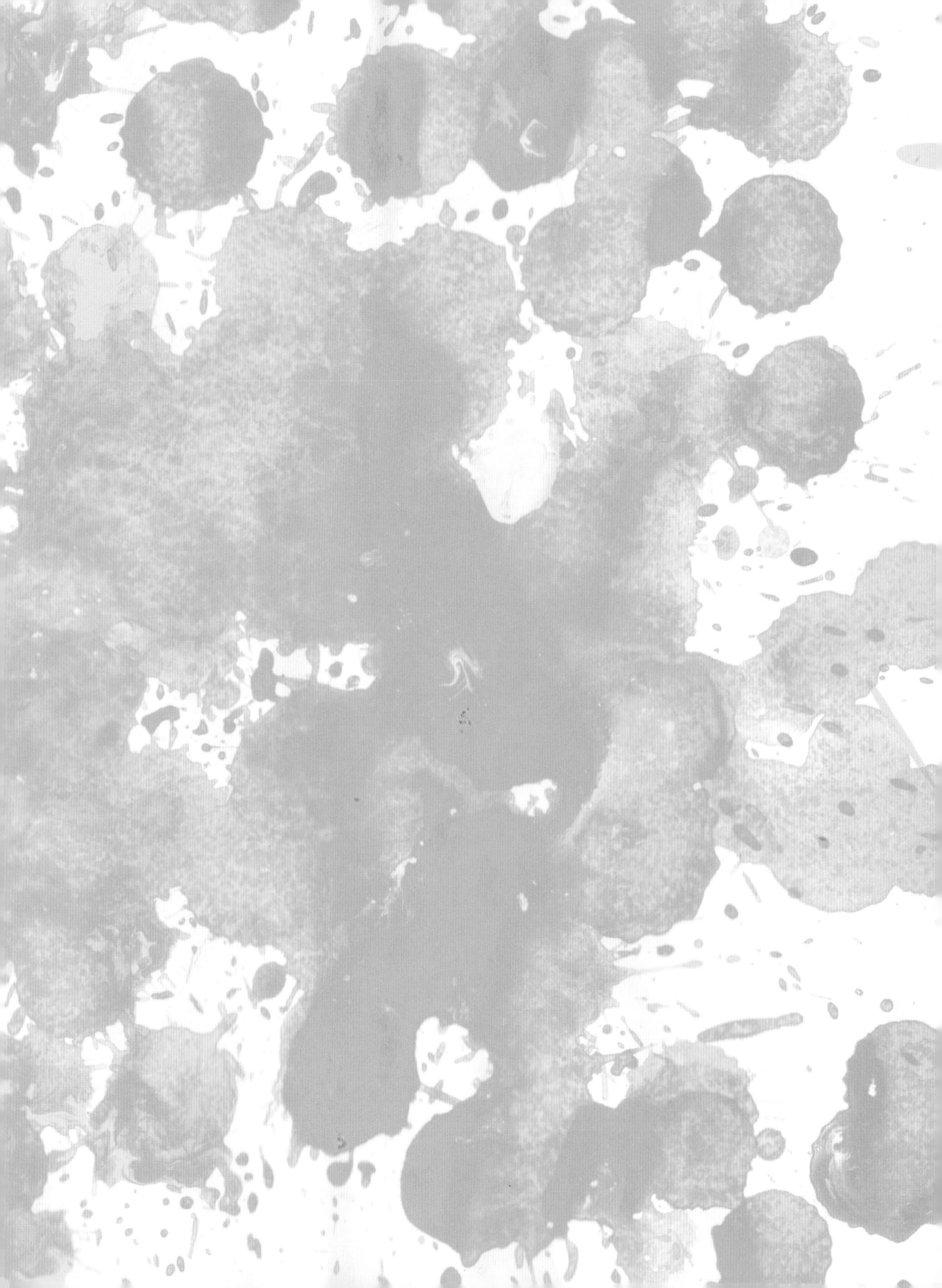

Unleash
your
creativity
on these
pages.

Draw a **night sky.**

Draw the last thing you **read.**

'You can't depend on your eyes when your imagination is out of focus.'

Mark Twain.

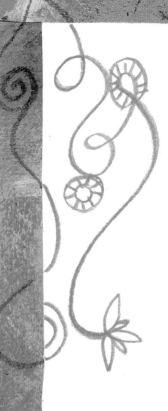

Fill these
pages with **doodles...**

can you do it without taking your
pencil off the page?

THINK OUTSIDE THE BOX AND COLOUR OUTSIDE THE LINES.

Draw a self-portrait using only **ZIGZAGGED** lines.

'There are no
only areas
against

lines in nature,
of colour, one
another.' Edouard Manet.

Draw a *thunderstorm.*

Draw something **furry.**

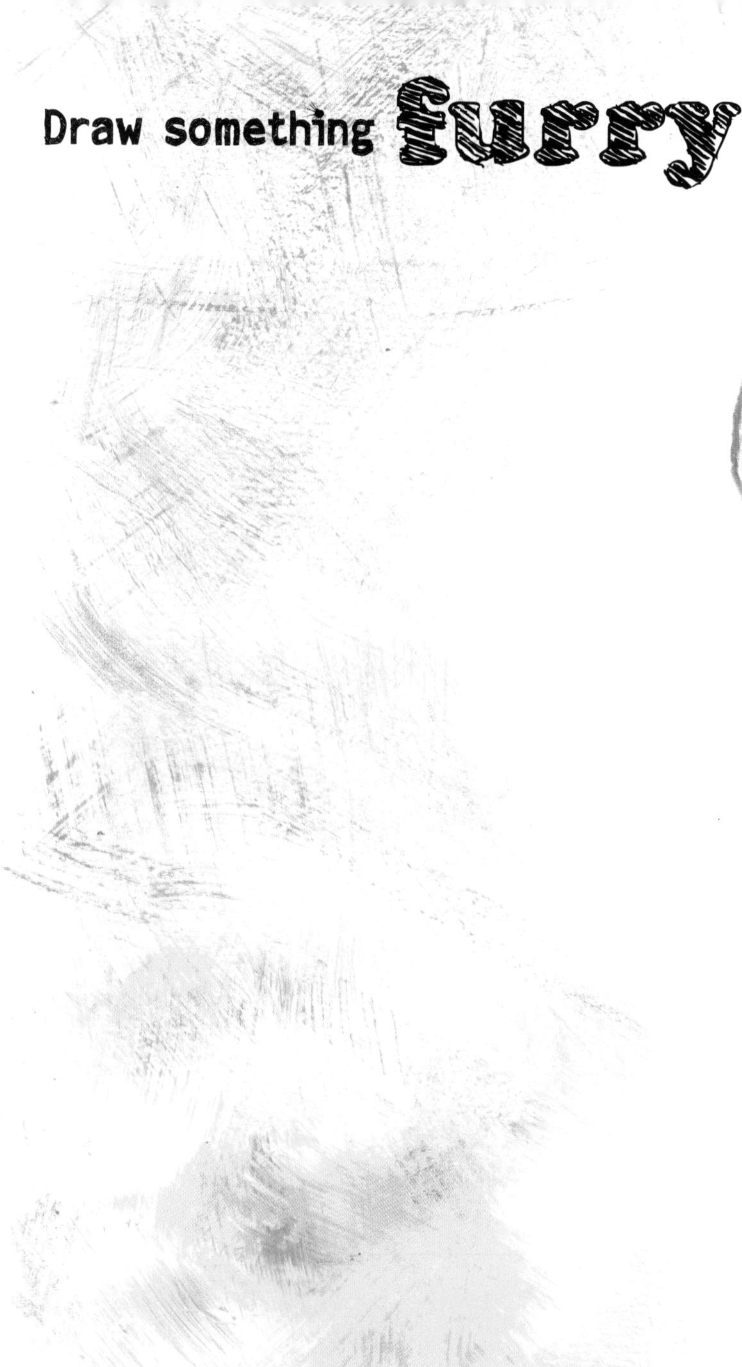

Draw an **animal** using only spiralling lines.

produces

Create!

Using black tones only,
draw a **FLOWER GARDEN.**

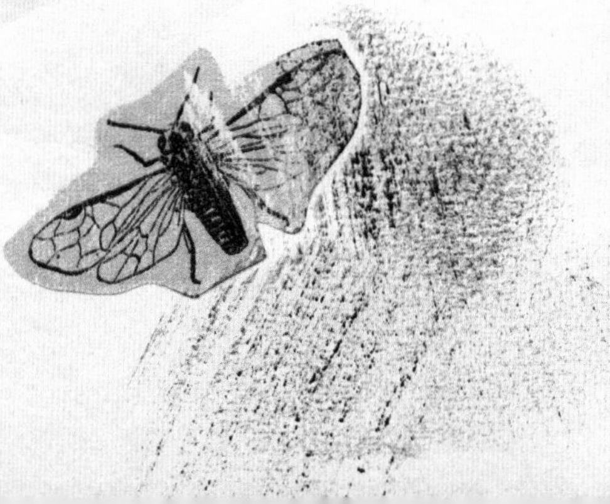

reversed

inverted

upside down

Using only letters, create a pattern.

inside out

back to front

Create a *list of words* about water.

SUBMERGE those
words into an ocean image.

Draw your *mood* using shapes only.

Draw an

angry colour.

Draw a **fight** between two colours.

Draw a **brawl** between four colours.

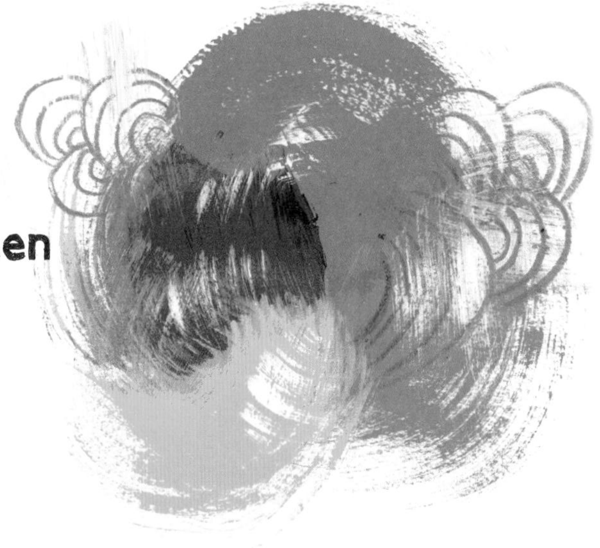

Draw the **inside** of your house from the **outside.**

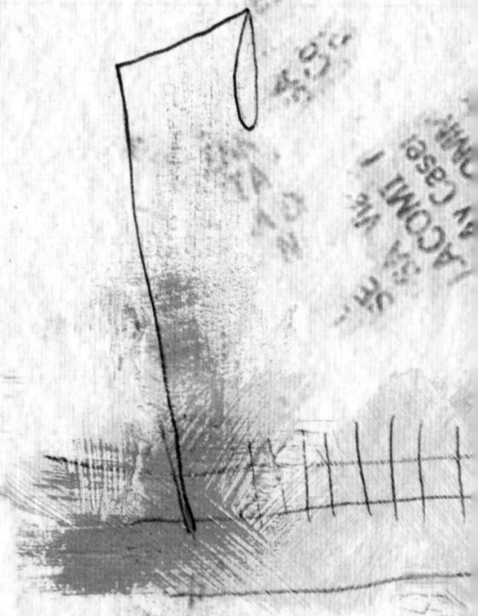

Draw, Paint
Sketch, Doodle
COLOUR

Shade
Outline, Depict
Illustrate
Scribble, Jot

DOODLE in or over the gridlines.

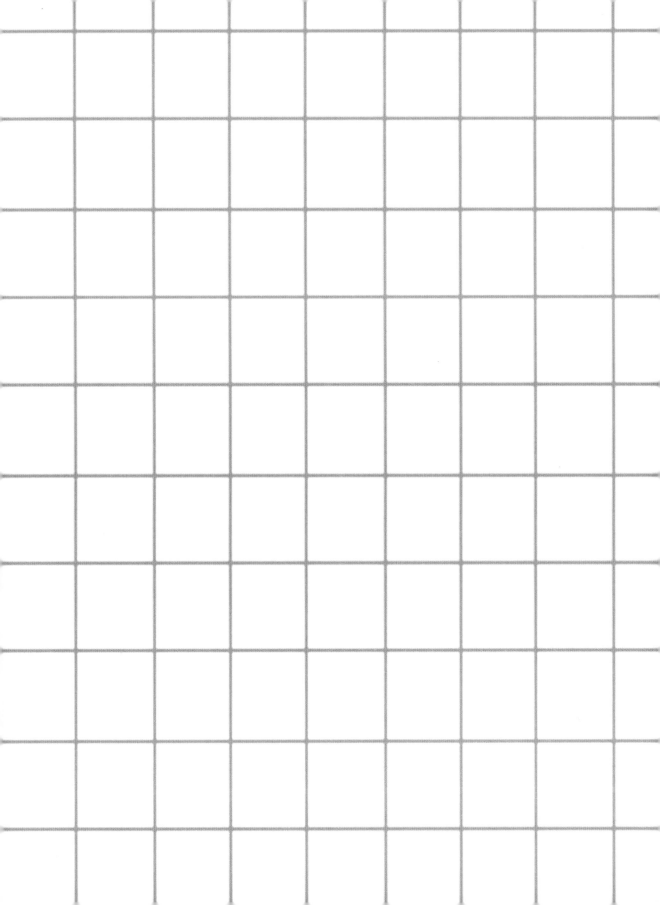

Doodles don't have to be mindless.

HB

CREATE ANYTHING!

Draw your hand using only

diagonal lines.

Draw a whirlpool of colour.

Draw a self-portrait from memory.

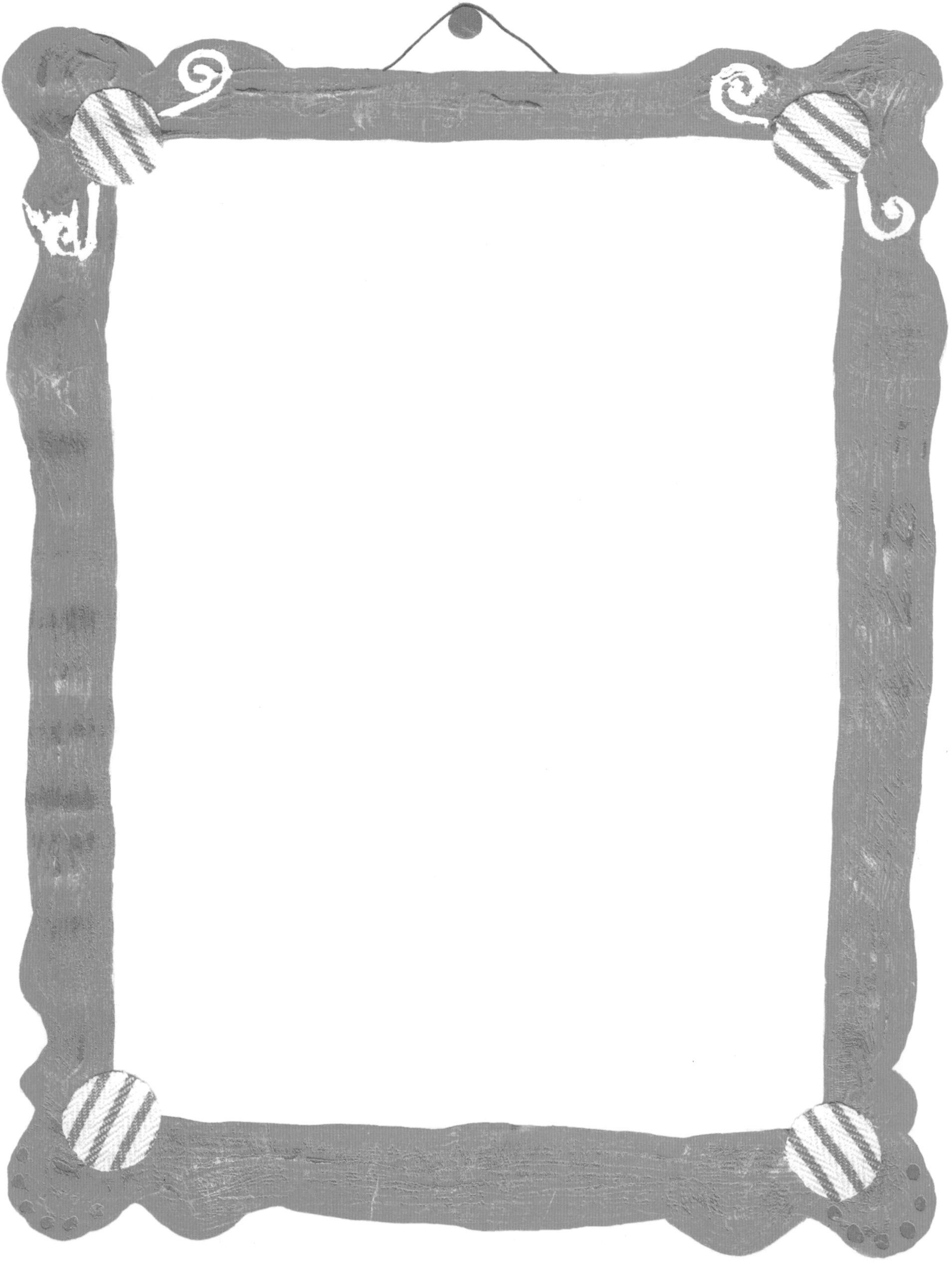

Draw a *self-portrait* using a mirror.

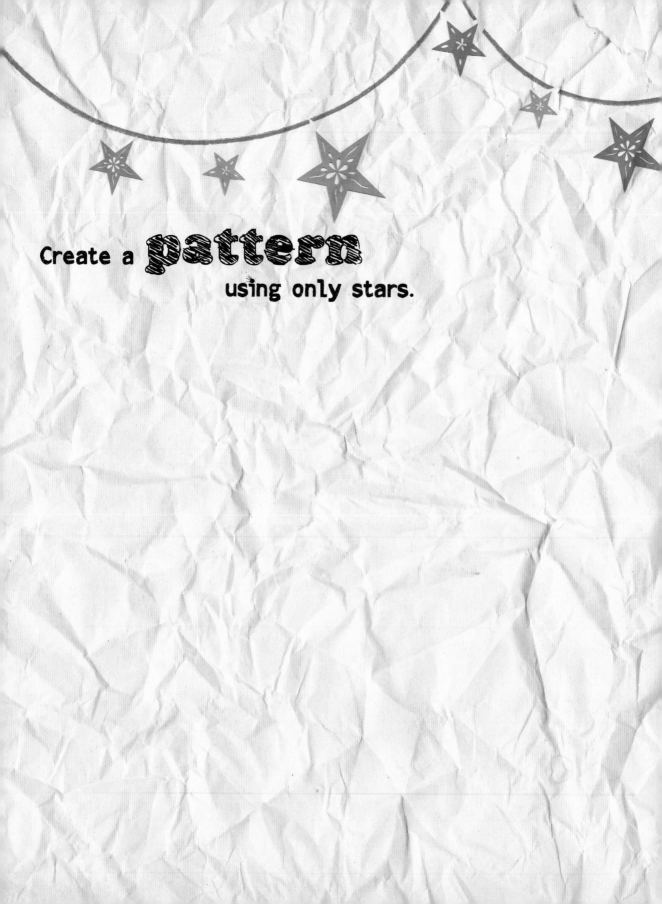

Create a **pattern** using only stars.

Personalize
this space.

Doodle without taking your pen off the paper.

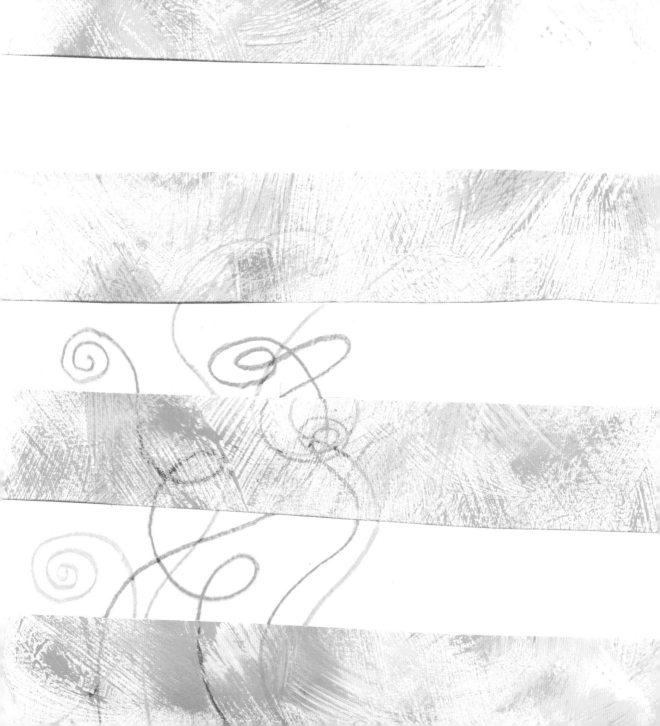

Try again in a
different colour.

And again?

'Even if you can't draw, do a little doodle or rip an illustration from a magazine. These visuals will help bring your idea to life.'

John Emmerling.

Fill these pages with

DIAMONDS.

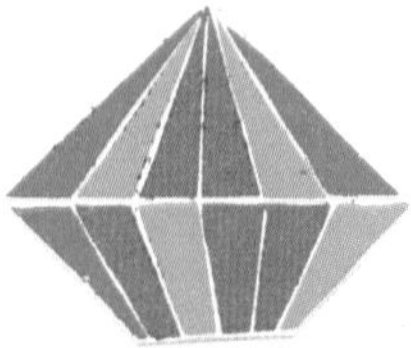

Draw fireworks.

Graffiti these pages.

Draw your home using only

wavy lines.

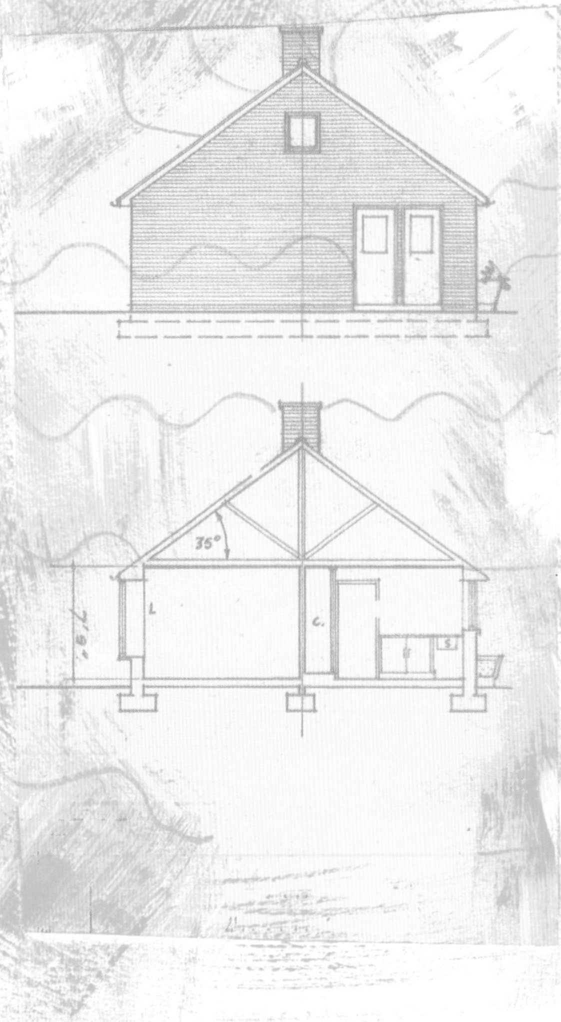

Fill these pages

with **SHAPES** that have

more than four sides.

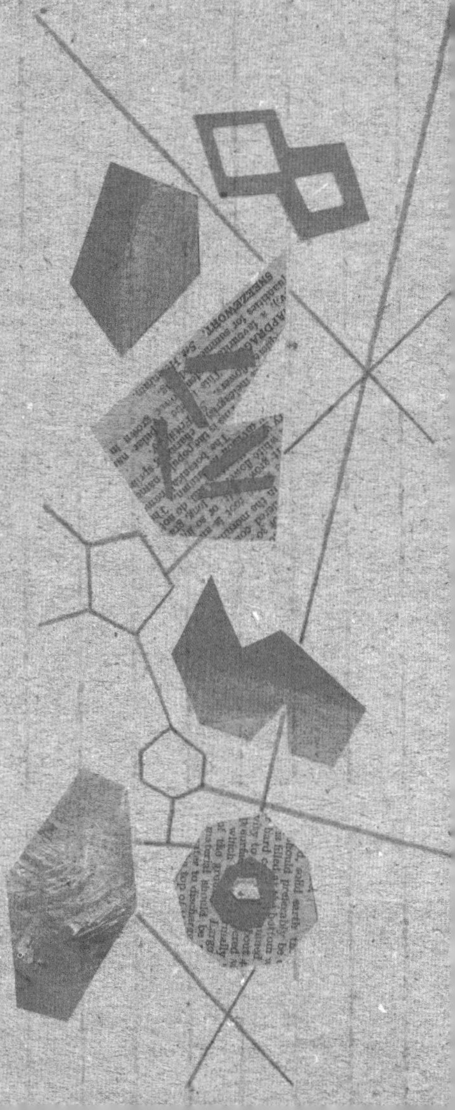

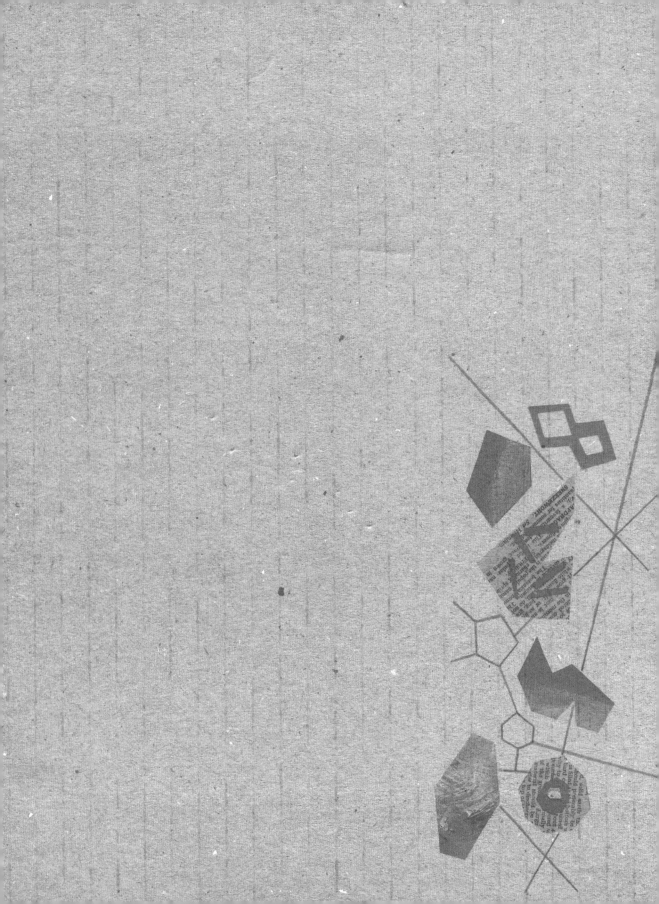

Draw the
view of
a room
as seen
through a

KEYHOLE.

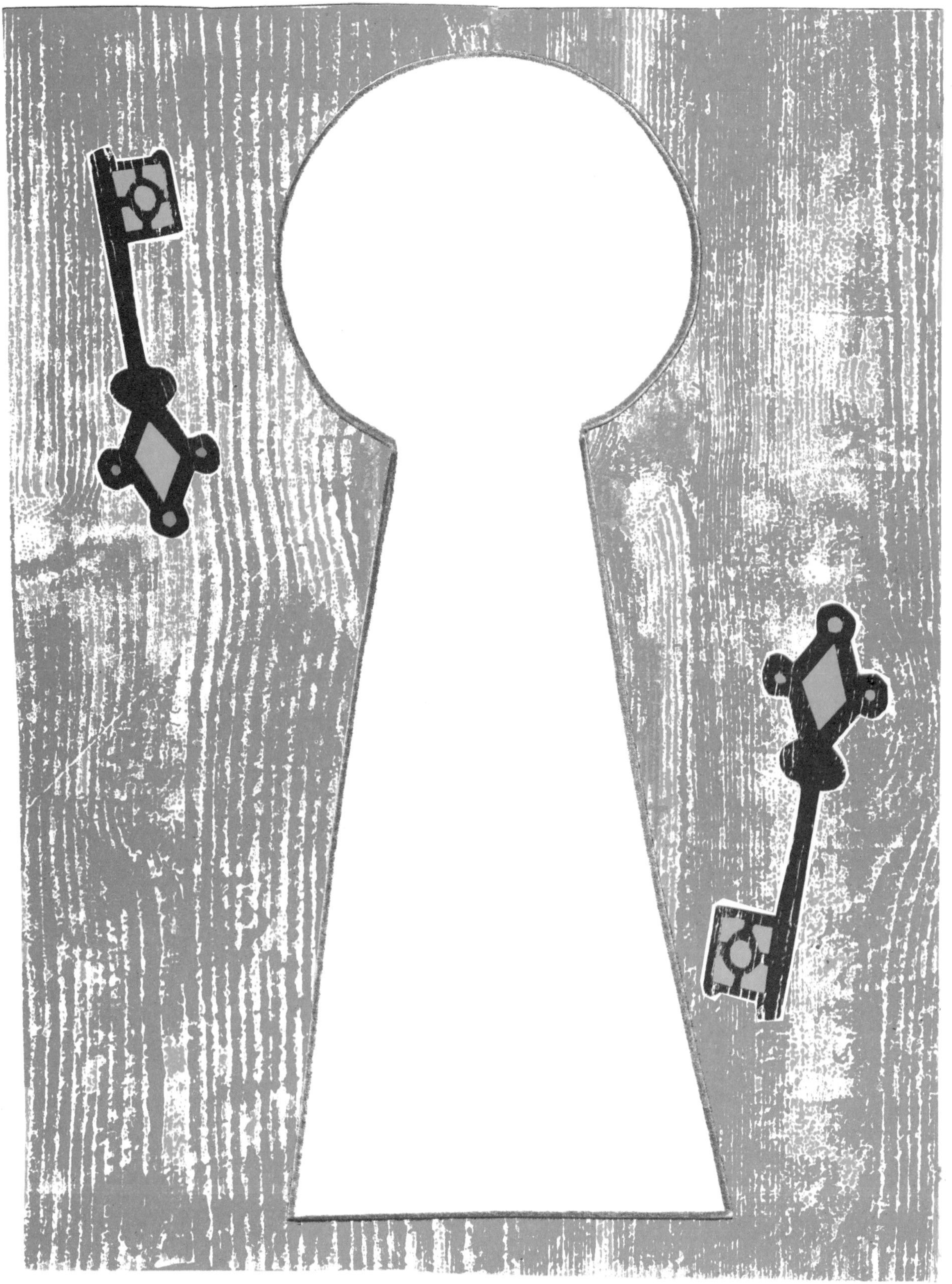

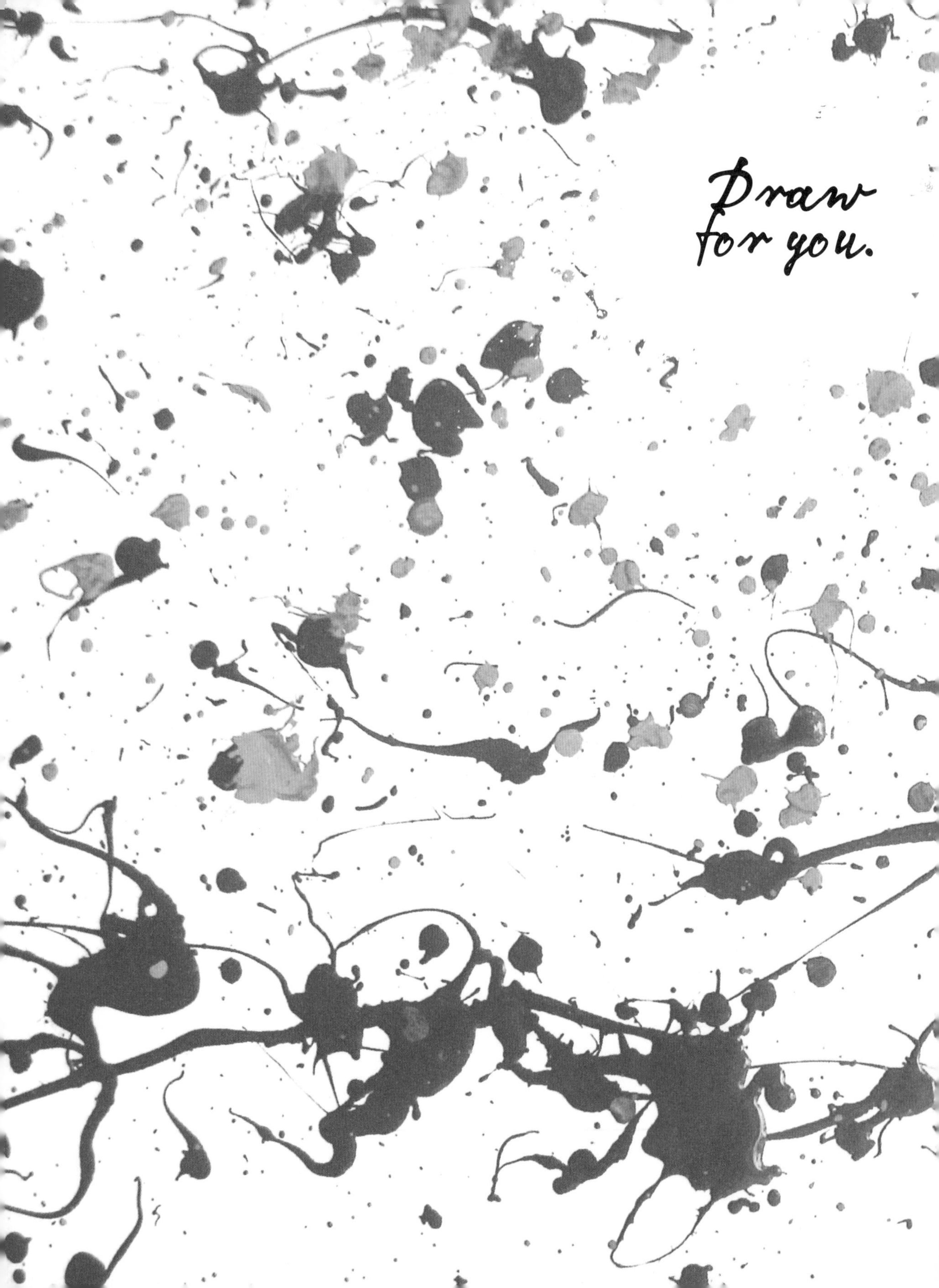
Draw
for you.

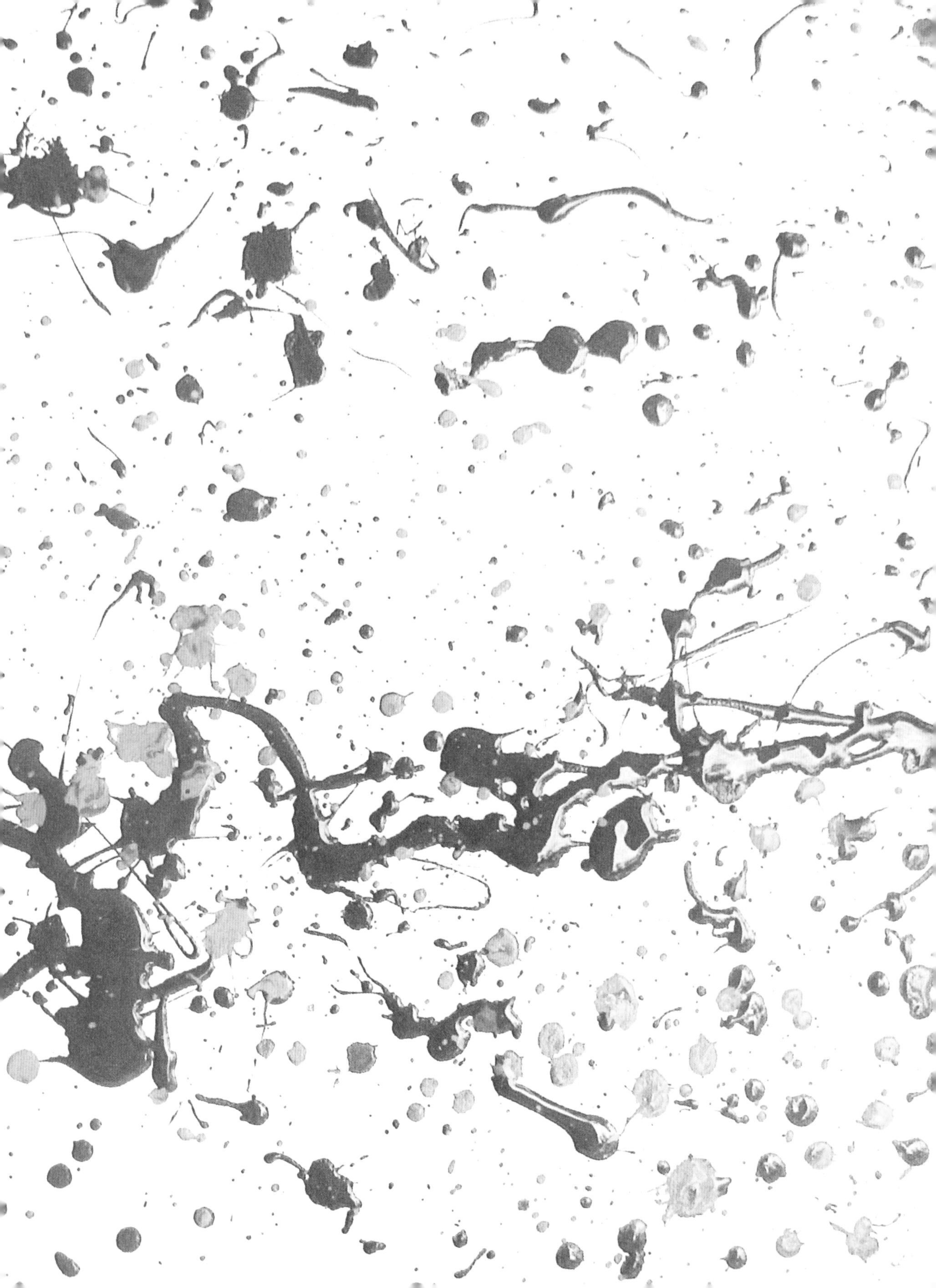

any suc
vacant s
can be
cut bac
their pr
March.
hausted branches can be
or additional branches
Short side growths should
untouched.
Fruiting spurs are kept
cutting back their new
annually,
stopping
nuts, of cou
inwards shoul
so that the bush
centre. Weakly
and any sucker g
should be remo
trees are pruned similarly. A clos
planted nut hedge will not be
to the same extent, but the sa
pruning princi
lowed.
The ideal bush tree carries
main framework of eight or
branches on a single stem of 12
to 15 in. in le
is trained to th
the manner explained fo
apples in the section H
PROPAGATE F
BUSH
ing
518

Fill these pages with

smoke.

SCRIBBLE!

Fill these pages with

spirals.

Draw your mood.

LOVE, SUBMISSION

REMORSE, CONTEM

OPTIMISM, SERE

APPREHENSIO

PENSIVENESS, BOR

INTEREST, JO

SURPRISE, SADNES

ANTICIPATION, ECS

TERROR, AMAZEME

RAGE, V

WE, DISAPPROVAL,
, AGGRESSIVENESS,
TY, ACCEPTANCE,
DISTRACTION,
OM, ANNOYANCE,
TRUST, FEAR,
DISGUST, ANGER,
ASY, ADMIRATION,
, GRIEF, LOATHING,
ILANCE.

Draw something coming out of this hole.

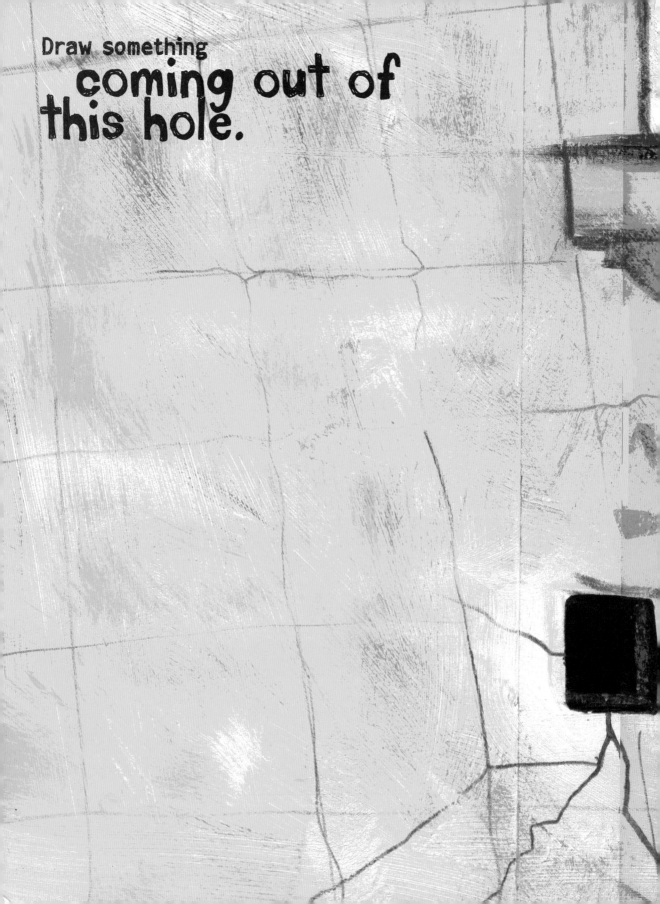

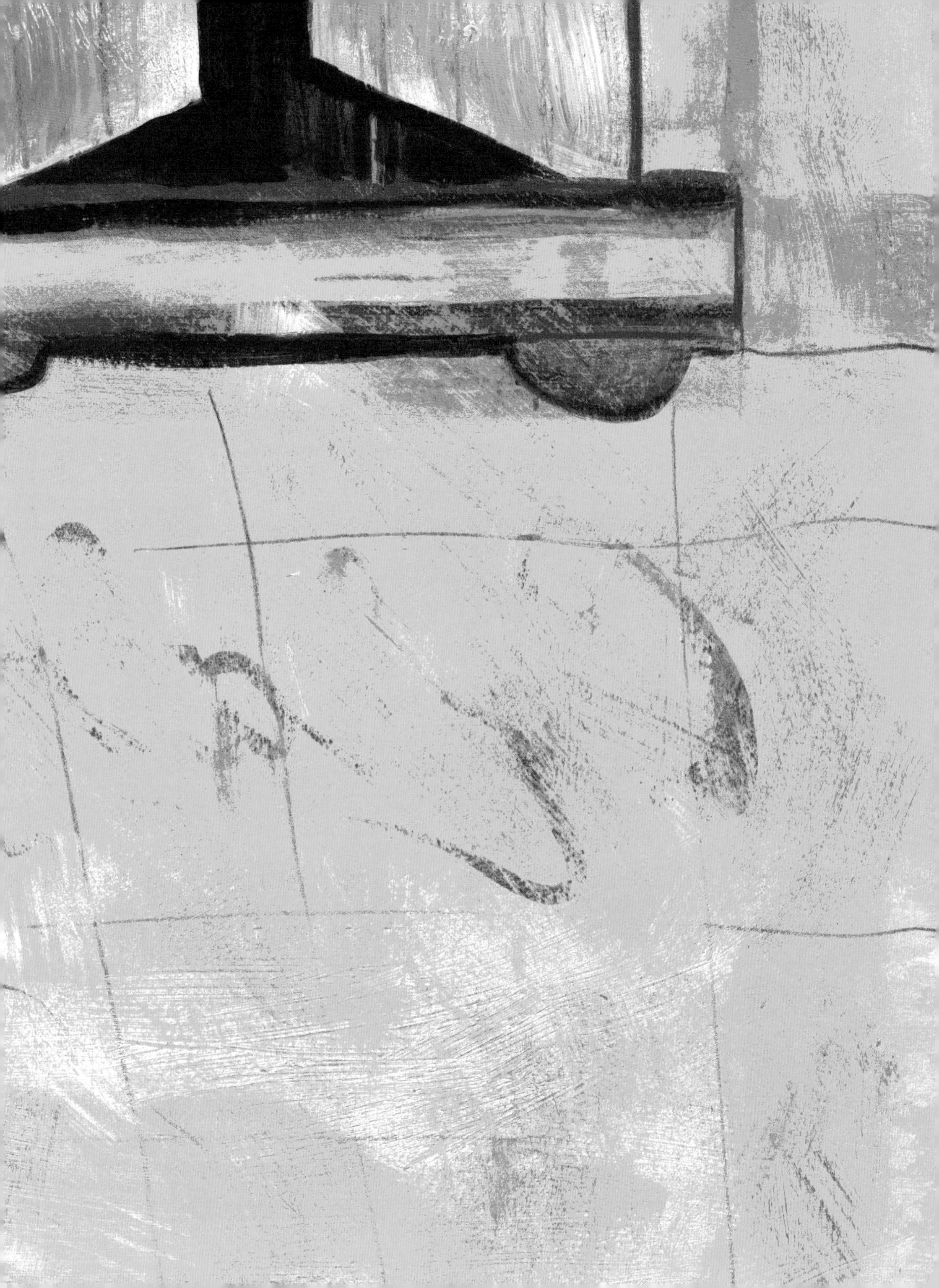

INSPIRE

YOURSELF.

Draw your

favourite song.

Draw the SOUNDS coming from this orchestra.

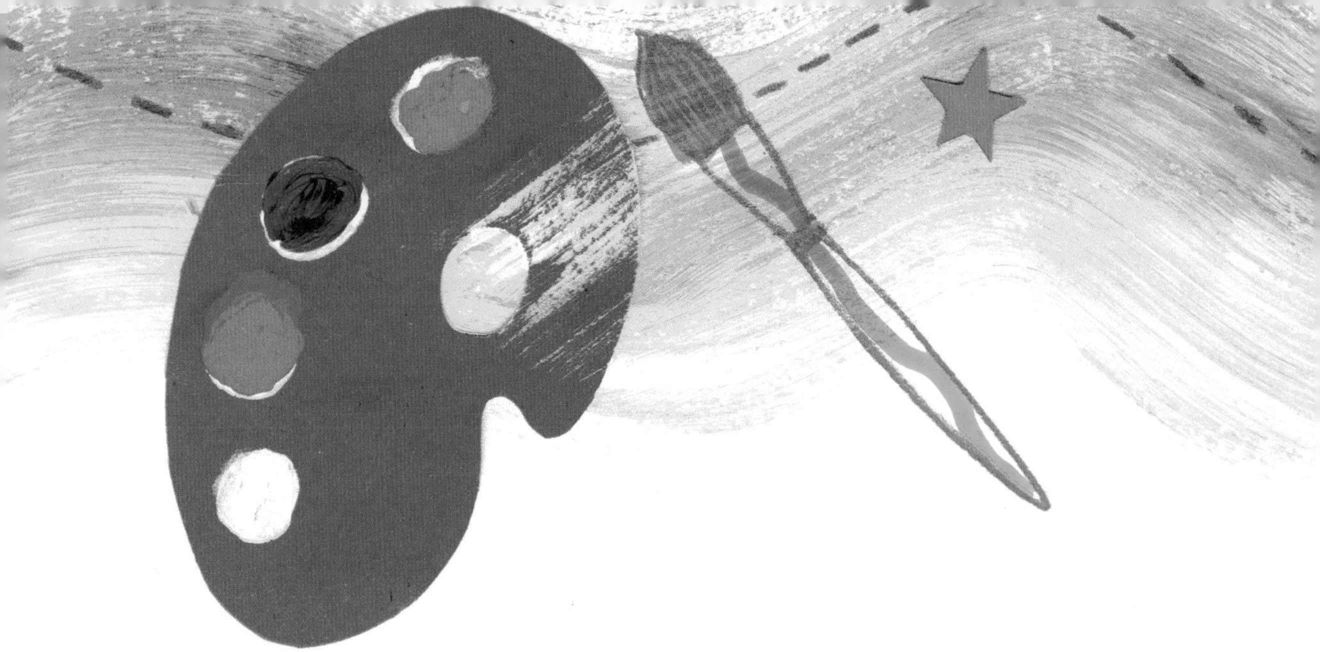

Fill these pages with

IDEAS.

'Creativity is allowing yourself to make mistakes. Art is knowing which ones to keep.' Scott Adams.